Contents

Run with me!

See you!

Um ... no thanks. You are too quick!

FLASH!

3

5

Just then ...

And the winner is ... wait and see!

Go to 10

Which Runner?

There are eight runners.
Which do you think is
the quickest?

12

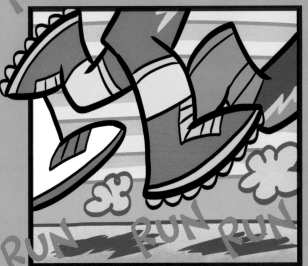

Mr Coach unveils the winner!

Her? Not fair!

The lemonade is on me!

Translate Backpack!

A-◎ B-↗ C-ぇ D-◩ E-ξ F-☼ G-⅓ H-⚡ I-ɛ
J-φ K-÷ L-★ M-🗎 N-◉ O-⊡ P-q Q-⚲ R-♄
S-▦ T-ℰ U-♕ V-◐ W-♡ X-⛰ Y-⛄ Z-☺

Can you translate what Backpack said in the comic?

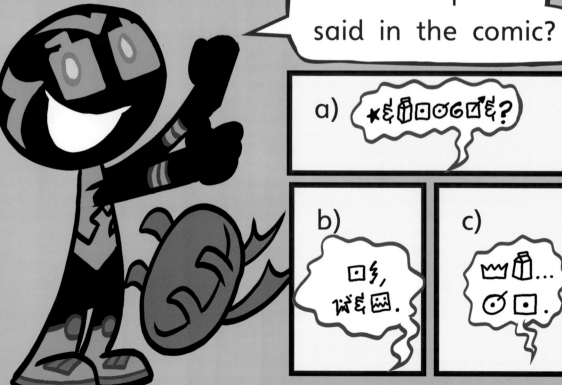

a) ★ξ🗎⊡◉◎◎◩ξ?

b) ⊡⚡,
⛄ξ▦.

c) ♕🗎...
◉⊡.

a) Lemonade. b) Oh, yes. c) Um … no.